Bojakaz Management, Ir
Missouri City, Texas
Copyright © 2012 by K. Akua Gray

This publication was designed to provide accurate and authoritative information in regard to the subject matters covered. It is sold with the intention to educate, inform and empower readers to make their own decisions on health, life and well being. If you have concerns about your physical, mental, emotional or spiritual condition, consult the appropriate professional of choice.

Graphic Design and Production: K. Akua Gray
Cover Design: K. Akua Gray
Photos: Akua Gray, Chenu Gray, ShanishkaBain
William Evertt – www.whiteclothphotography.com
Published by: Bojakaz Management, Inc.
P.O. Box 921, Missouri City, TX 77459

Printed in the United States of America

ISBN: 978-0-615-370-934

Table of Contents

Midday Magic for Maximum Health

Divine Desserts and Drinks

Transition Recipes

Acknowledgements

Give thanks to the creator whose sustaining energy supplies my life.

To the spirit of the ancestors whose guiding presence and earthly teachings have supplied me with love, knowledge and the determination to be the spirit that I am today. Rita Piper, Garry Piper, Elvin Leigh, Roosevelt Morgan, Katie Love, Robert Lee, Pascal Leigh, Martha Lee, Susan Lee, Cousin Leona Rita Lee, Mary Robinson Lee, Hattie Moore, Jesse Praiter, Shatawa, Baba and all the ancestors I do not know and whose blood runs through my veins who lived by good character during their times here on earth, I call your names and honor you with my whole being!

To my husband G. Chenu Gray, my sons Kazembe, Jaja, Bomani, Granny Ella Gray, who have supported me in every idea and endeavor that has ever been given to me to pursue, I say THANK YOU!

And thank you for allowing me to share this peace knowledge with you so that the circle of love and healing continues.

-Dr. Akua Gray

Preface

In the pages of this book, I have given you an outline to work with to enhance your knowledge of a healthy eating lifestyle. I say enhance because the first step is having and acting on a sincere desire to change from the old destructive ways of eating to live foods for maximum nutrition and wellness. So, this book is for seekers, those who have reached a certain level in divine consciousness.

I have included recipes for maximum nutrition, recipes to consider when certain ailments are present, recipes to intake particular nutrients and many other tips for growth and positive change for you, your family and your community.

The world can't hide anything from the people anymore, because we are reading and growing and living and loving and preparing for the spiritual revolution that will change existence for peace and progress.

Also, these are some of my favorite creations and I can eat them every day because they are sooooo good! Smile.

- K. Akua Gray

Introduction

My coming to eating healthy and holistically was a long road traveled. The creator had this journey in mind for me at a very early age. Many angels were put in my path to teach me the ways of the earth and the blessings of abundance that comes from within.

I grew up on the typical diet of the black family in an urban area, however, my father would always stress to us the importance of eating real meat. He, himself, did not eat pork, but beef all the time. My mother didn't agree with him, so she fed us everything. Shortly after reaching adulthood, my brother Garry came home and told me the story of the trichinae worm and why I should not eat pork and, of course, it brought back from memory all that my father had told us through the years. So, you know for little sisters, if your big brother said it then it was something to listen to. That became the beginning of my consciousness to a lifestyle of healthy eating.

From there, over the next 18 years, yes it has taken 18 years to reach this point in my journey to knowledgeable holistic eating. The gradual changes included releasing all flesh, dairy products, fast foods, sweets, processed foods, non-organic foods and destructive methods of food preparation.

Introduction to Food Science

Some of us never take the time to even consider the facts of what keeps our bodies going on a daily basis. We have been numbed by society to only focus on the outward physical appearance and that leaves us unconscious of the requirements of the interior. Everything that manifest on a physical level in our lives is first manifested on the unseen level and that includes our physical bodies. This is why we suffer from so many diseases and ailments. We have yet to grasp the knowledge of taking care of ourselves on the unseen level first. Just the idea of looking inside the body is not appealing to most, so we often neglect the requirements that our inner body needs to keep us healthy. The human anatomy is one of the most beautifully complex systems that you can study. It is a true testament to the omnipotence of the creator. The body temple houses enumerable functions and faculties that allow us to live our lives to the fullest even when we don't nourish and treat these divine sanctuaries with the respect they deserve. So, let us take just a moment to touch the surface of our anatomy (structure) and our physiology (function) of this vessel of love and power that we call body.

Why do you eat?

Starting with the basic component of our anatomy, which is really the most important because it makes up our entire being, we look at the cell.

Cells
The cell is the basic structural and functional component of life. Humans have 60-100 trillion cells. Cells carry out the most vital functions of the body, such as metabolism, growth, adaptability, repair and reproduction. The body also contains distinct kinds of cells, each with specialized functions. You have bone cells, muscle cells, fat cells, blood cells and nerve cells. Water is the most abundant compound in every cell.

Tissues
The tissues of your body are layers of similar cells that perform a specific function. Your heart muscle and your outer layer of skin are examples of tissue.

Organs
An organ is two or more tissues combined to perform a particular function. There are many organs in the body, for example; the heart, spleen, pancreas, ovary, bones and stomach. They have primary and secondary tissue to carry out its function in the body.

Systems

The body systems consist of various organs that have a similar function. Your body systems are:

Integumentary System – external support and protection of the body (skin, hair, etc.)

Skeletal System – internal support and flexible framework for body movement and production of blood cells

Muscular System – body movement; production of body heat

Lymphatic System – body immunity; absorption of fats; drainage of tissue fluids

Urinary System – filtration of blood; maintenance of volume and chemical composition of the blood; removal of metabolic waste from the body

Endocrine System – secretion of hormones for chemical regulation

Nervous System – regulation of all body activities; learning and memory

Respiratory System – gaseous exchange between external environment and blood

Circulatory System – transport of life sustaining materials to body cells; removal of metabolic wastes from cells

Digestive System – breaking down and absorption of food materials

Female Reproductive System – production of female sex cells (ova); receptacle of sperm from male; site of fertilization of ovum, implantation, and development of embryo and fetus; delivery of fetus

Male Reproductive System – production of male sex cells (sperm); transfer of sperm to reproductive system of female

These systems of your body are the only reason food should be important to you. It's time to gently take your mind to another level of living your life to the fullest.

Water

The most important food for our systems is H^2O, because water makes up 60% of every cell in our body. It is the primary life substance needed for you and your children to be healthy.

Your body uses water for the digestion, absorption and transport of nutrients. It dilutes your bodies waste by reducing the waste's toxicity and aids in excreting the waste from the body. Water regulates the temperature of the body through your sweat glands. It keeps your skin soft and smooth.

If you don't give your body enough water, it becomes dehydrated and toxic. A toxic body is a haven for disease and ailments. When the body is in a toxic state, its pH is either too acidic or overly alkaline.

The body's potential for hydrogen (pH), which is basically how much water is available in your body for the function of your cells, is at a healthy level at 6.4. Below 6.4 is considered acidic, and above 6.4 is alkaline.

All foods also have a pH level and it is best for your health to eat a balance of acid and alkaline foods.

Some alkaline foods include:

Apricot	Watermelon	Potato
Apple	Beet	Pumpkin
Avocado	Strawberry	Sea
Banana	Bell pepper	vegetables
Blackberry	Broccoli	Squash
Blueberry	Brussels	Sweet
Cantaloupe	sprouts	Potato
Cherry	Burdock	Taro root
Currant	Kohlrabi	Turnips
Dewberry	Cauliflower	Yam
Grape	Chives	Lentils
Grapefruit	Collards	Oats
Honeydew	Daikon	Quinoa
Lemon	Eggplant	Almonds
Loganberry	Endive	Flax seeds
Mango	Ginger root	Poppy seeds
Nectarine	Kale	Pumpkin
Lime	Mustard	seeds
Orange	Greens	Sunflower
Papaya	Garlic	Seeds
Pear	Lentil	Avocado oil
Persimmon	Lettuce	Coconut oil
Peach	Mushroom	Flax oil
Raisins	Okra	Olive oil
Raspberry	Onion	Primrose oil
Pineapple	Parsley	Sesame oil
Tangerine	Parsnip	

Some acid foods include:

Cranberry	Fig	Pomegranate
Date	Guava	Prune
Dried fruit	Plum	Tomato

Carrots
Chard
Chutney
Rhubarb
Spinach
Aduki beans
Chickpea
Fava beans
Green pea
Kidney
beans
Lima beans
Navy beans
Peanut
Pinto beans

Snow pea
Soy beans
String beans
Tofu
White beans
Amaranth
Barley
Brown rice
Buckwheat
Corn
Millet
Oat bran
Brazil nut
Hazelnut
Pecan

Pine nuts
Pistachio
Walnut
Spelt
Rye
Wheat
Pumpkin seed
oil
Grape seed oil
Sunflower oil
Almond oil
Sesame oil
Safflower oil

When the body is acidic, it is a haven for disease. Cancer can only survive in an acid environment along with most other diseases. A body that is overly alkaline can create an environment where the internal organs are stressed and there could be system failure. A pH imbalance is specific to the inability to use carbohydrates and fats. It produces gland problems in the endocrine system in such glands as the adrenal, thyroid and pituitary. Kidney and respiratory problems can also result. The body's hormonal levels are affected in the levels of progesterone, estrogen and testosterone. Maintaining a healthy pH means being conscious of what you put in your body and taking the preventative measure of checking your own pH periodically to monitor your levels.

Nutrients

What you need to feed your body-
Vitamins, minerals, enzymes, amino acids, etc...

Vitamins are the components of nutrition that the body needs to function and regenerate itself. The body does not need a large amount of vitamins, however, a lack of any certain one can cause a deficiency which can then results in malfunctions in specific areas of the body's systems. Knowing what your body needs is a big step to understanding how to stay healthy. Vitamins should be taken into the body through the foods that you eat. However, because of the standard diet of overcooked, toxic-filled and denatured foods that our family consumes, most eating lifestyles require a dietary supplement in the form of a multivitamin to supply the body with adequate nutrients. If you elect to take a multivitamin, make sure it is derived from a natural, plant-based source. Synthetically- produced vitamins have added chemicals that alter the body's natural function and could be dangerous if taken in excessive amounts resulting in vitamin poisoning called hypervitaminosis.

This section is intended to give you general information on the different types of vitamins and minerals.

Vitamin A - Beta Carotene is a plant-based source found in most vegetables that helps prevent infections, boosts immune function which protects against diseases such as influenza and cancers. Vitamin A forms and maintains healthy skin by preventing acne, it slows the process of aging and is needed for skin and tissue repair. Vitamin A promotes healthy hair, is essential in cell growth and development, and mucous membranes such as healing and preventing gastro-intestinal ulcers. Vitamin A aids vision in dim light or night blindness and maintains healthy eyesight.

The animal source of Vitamin A is also known as retinol and can be found in animal liver. However, your best source is plant based.

Vitamin A is not needed in large amounts and can cause toxicity in the body if taken in large amounts. The optimal daily intake amount is 5,000 – 15,000 IU. Sources of vitamin A are plentiful in the natural foods that you eat: alfalfa, apricots, asparagus, broccoli, beets, cabbage, cantaloupe, carrots, dandelion greens, garlic, grapefruit, greens (all types), kale, mango, mustard, nori (seaweed), oranges, papaya, parsley, peppers, peaches, pumpkin, spirulina, yellow squash, tomatoes, turnip greens, watermelon and watercress.

Vitamin A is made in your liver using beta carotene as a precursor that combines with cryptoxanthin, a provitamin.

Vitamin B1 – Thiamin is used by the body forcarbohydrates conversion for energy; it breaks down fats and protein, aids in digestion, nervous

17

system function, skin, hair, eyes, mouth, liver health and immune system function. Vitamin B1 is known to be vital in heart health, slowing age related cognitive decline like Alzheimer's and fatigue. Sources of vitamin B1 are whole grain breads and cereals, dried beans and peas.

Vitamin B2 - Riboflavin assists with metabolism and carbohydrate conversion: it breaks down fat and protein, aids in digestion, nervous system function, is good for skin, hair, eyes, mouth, liver and assists in the formation of red blood cells (RBC). Concerns that may arise due to a lack of this nutrient are anemia, decreased free radical protection, cataracts, poor thyroid function, B6 deficiency and fatigue. Sources include dark green vegetables, whole grain breads and cereals.

Vitamin B3 - Niacinenhances your energy, digestion, nervous system, skin, hair, eyes and liver. Vitamin B3 eliminates toxins, assists in the health of sex and stress hormones, improves circulation, cracking and scaling skin, digestive problems confusion, anxiety and fatigue. Sources include whole grains, bulgar, oatmeal, nuts, dried beans and peas.

Vitamin B6 - Pyroxidineprovides enzyme protein metabolism, RBC production, formation of nerve and muscle tissue, DNA/RNA, B12 absorption, immune function and brain function. A deficiency could result in depression, sleep and skin problems, confusion, anxiety and fatigue. Sources include

18

dried beans, peas, nuts, whole grain breads, cereals and bananas.

Vitamin B12 – Cobalamin provides healthy nerve cells, DNA/RNA, red blood cell production and iron function. Deficiencies can result in anemia, fatigue, constipation, loss of appetite or weight, numbness and tingling in hands and feet, depression, dementia, poor memory and oral soreness. Sources include fortified vegetable and grain products.

Vitamin A - Retinol helps prevent infections; helps form and maintain healthy skin, hair and mucous membranes. It aids vision in dim light, the eyes, immune system function, essential cell growth and development, zinc deficiency and fat malabsorption. Sources include deep yellow, orange and dark green vegetables and fruit such as carrots, broccoli, spinach, sweet potatoes, pumpkin, winter squash and cantaloupe.

Vitamin C - Ascorbic acid is needed for collagen, a substance that holds body cells together including bones, cartilage, muscle and vascular tissue. It helps maintain capillaries, teeth, speeds up the healing of wounds and damaged bones, aids in iron absorption and helps protects other vitamins from oxidation. Vitamin C is excellent in cleansing toxins from the body, preventing dental cavities, crooked teeth, inflammation of gums and Integumentary inflammations. Sources are citrus fruits, berries, melons, dark-green vegetables, tomatoes, green peppers, cabbage and potatoes.

Vitamin D – Calciferolhelps form and maintains bones and teeth, calcium and phosphorus absorption, bone mineralization. If a deficiency is experienced, bone loss, osteoporosis and thyroid problems may occur. Vitamin D is made by the body when it's exposed to sunlight. Fifteen to thirty minutes of exposure everyday is recommended and should add an adequate supply to the average person. Vitamin D as a food source is found in certain fish, milk is fortified with vitamin D, and it does not occur naturally in cow's milk.

Vitamin E – Tocopherolis an antioxidant; it regulates oxidation reactions, stabilizes cell membrane, aids immune system functions, protects against cardiovascular disease, cataracts and macular degeneration, assist with a healthy Integumentary system and prevents rupturing red blood cells. If a deficiency is present, anemia, bruising, PMS, hot flashes, eczema, psoriasis, wounds healing may become difficult, muscle weakness and sterility may be experienced. Food sources include nuts, vegetable oils, wheat germ, whole grain breads and cereals and green leafy vegetables.

Vitamin K – Phylioquinone helps synthesize substances needed for blood clotting, maintenance of normal bone metabolism. Deficiency indicators are red spots around coiled hair follicles, bruises in the skin due to capillary fragility, cortical hemorrhages of bone visible on x-ray, hemorrhages in skin and gastrointestinal problems. Food sources include spinach and other green leafy vegetables, cabbage, broccoli, cauliflower, tomatoes and whole wheat. Vitamin K is made in the body by bacteria in the intestines. Supplementation is rarely needed. It is given to infants at birth "to prevent hemorrhaging".

Boron is a trace mineral that assist in the prevention of bone loss. It also assists the body to maintain minerals such as calcium, magnesium and phosphorus. Studies show boron is evident in mental alertness, muscle growth, fat and sugar conversion and the body's steroid production. Boron is present in most fruits and vegetables namely apples, carrots, dark greens, grapes, nuts, pears and whole grains.

Calciumis basicallyneeded for every function in the body. Calcium is stored in the bones and is released into the body as needed to strengthen and support the teeth, the heart, nerves, muscles and all body systems. Calcium, however, needs other nutrients to function. Deficiencies in calcium are evident in osteoporosis, osteomalacia, osteoarthritis, muscle cramps, irritability, acute anxiety and colon cancer. Food sources include turnip greens, bokchoy, okra, mustard greens, kale, broccoli, oats, white beans, navy beans, black beans, chick peas, pinto beans etc. Because calcium is a major component in soil, it is present in most fruits and vegetables.

Chromium is needed in the body for energy. It is vital in glucose metabolism and the synthesis of cholesterol, fats and proteins as well. Chromium is also important in the maintaining a health blood sugar level. Chromium deficiency is common because it is depleted in most soils and most diets do not support the intake of chromium rich foods like brown rice, corn, dried beans, mushrooms, potatoes and whole grains.

Copper, although a minute amount, is needed for the body is used in several systems of the body. In the circulatory system, copper helps form red blood cells. In the Integumentary system, it is involved in the form of skin and hair and skin color. In the skeletal system, it helps in the formation of bones, and the same with the muscular system, it helps in joint health and collagen formation. Signs of deficiency include anemia, balding, diarrhea, fatigue, osteoporosis and skin problems. An excessive copper supplement intake can be fatal. It is recommended to eat copper rich foods for the proper amount. Copper can be found in nuts like almonds and pecans. Fruits like oranges and raisins supply an adequate amount. Vegetables containing copper are avocados, beets, broccoli, dark leafy greens, garlic and radishes. Other sources include barley, blackstrap molasses, lentils, mushrooms and soybeans.

Folic Acid helps form hemoglobin in red blood cells and aids in the formation of genetic materials. Deficiencies includes anemia, digestive disorders such as diarrhea and loss of appetite, headaches, heart palpitations and forgetfulness. Food sources include cereals, dark green leafy vegetables, dried beans and peas, fruits (especially fresh squeezed orange juice) and whole grain breads.

Iron is vital for blood formation, energy production and a healthy immune system. Deficiencies include anemia, bone and hair loss, brittle hair, dizziness, fatigue, inflammation and nerve issues. Excellent food sources include avocados, beets, dates, dulse, kelp, beans, lentils, peaches, pears, prunes, raisin, rice, sesame seeds, soybeans and wheat bran.

Magnesium is responsible for about 300 biochemical reactions including muscle and nerve functions, heart rhythm, immune system, strong bones, calcium, copper, potassium, vitamin D and zinc regulation. Deficiencies include a loss of appetite, cramps, fatigue, heart spasms, nausea, numbness, personality changes, seizures and vomiting. Foods sources include almonds, artichokes, beans, bran, nuts, oats, okra, pumpkin, quinoa, spinach and squash.

Manganese is needed for blood sugar regulation, bone growth, energy, healthy nerves, immune system health and protein and fat metabolism. Deficiencies include eye problems, hearing problems, heart problems, high cholesterol, hypertension, irritability, memory loss and pancreas stress. Food sources include avocado, blueberries, green veggies, legumes, nuts, pineapple, seaweeds, seeds and whole grains.

Phosphorus is needed for utilizing carbohydrates, fats and protein. It also assists with bone growth and energy production. Deficiencies include anxiety, breath abnormality, fatigue, pain in the bones and general body weakness. Food sources include asparagus, bran, brewer's yeast, corn, garlic, legumes, nuts, seeds (sesame, sunflower and pumpkin) and whole grain.

Potassium aids in heart regulation, blood pressure health, nervous system health and works with sodium to control the body's water balance. Deficiencies include acne, constipation, depression, diarrhea, edema, glucose intolerance, headaches, insomnia, low blood pressure, nervousness, proteinuria and salt retention. Food sources include apricots, avocado, banana, Brewer's yeast, brown rice, dates, figs, garlic, nuts, potatoes, raisins, spinach, winter squash, wheat bran and yams.

Selenium is anantioxidant that works with vitamin E and is necessary for proper immune system function, tumor prevention and thyroid health. It is also beneficial for heart and liver health. Deficiencies could cause destruction of the heart and pancreas, sore muscles, fragility of red blood cells, immune system weakness. Food sources include Brazil nuts, Brewer's yeast, broccoli, brown rice, dulse, garlic, oats, onions, whole wheat breads and cereals.

COQ10is a powerful antioxidant, it stops oxidation of LDL cholesterol, assists in energy production, also known for its anti-aging properties, is important to heart, liver and kidney health. Ailments associated with deficiencies include

24

cardiac arrhythmias, congestive heart failure, diabetes, fatigue, gingivitis, high blood pressure, a poor immune system and stroke. Food sources include broccoli, fish, nuts and spinach.

Zincsupports enzymes, immune system health, wound healing, DNA synthesis, normal growth and development during pregnancy, childhood and adolescence. Growth retardation, hair loss, diarrhea, impotence, eye and skin lesions, loss of appetite, weight loss, wounds that are not easy to heal and mental lethargy are signs of deficiency. Food sources include beans, legumes, nuts, rice, seeds and whole grains.

When we know better, we do better. This information is strictly for education purposes only. It is in no way distributed to be medical advice and any changes in your diet should be discussed with your health care provider.

In Your Health Foods Kitchen

Your kitchen should always be clean and well sanitized, using natural methods of cleaning and disinfecting such as castile detergents and soaps, lavender oil, lemon juice and oil, vinegar and peppermint oil. There are also many non-toxic cleaners now available in your local health foods market. This is the most important room in your house for the nourishment of your longevity and health. Your food is your medicine, your food is your energy, your food is your body builder and your food is your mechanical life force.

Some helpful tools and equipment that you should have in your live foods kitchen are:

Water filter system
Juicer
Blender
Food processor
Spiral slicer
Small citrus juicer
Sharp knives
Wood cutting boards
Mixing bowls various sizes
Platters various sizes
Mixing spoons
Tongs
Glass pitcher
Grater
Mason jars
Cheesecloth
Strainer
Spice jars
Rectangular glass pans
Small handy chopper
Measuring cups
Measuring spoons
Vegetable scrub brush
Dehydrator
Veggie Wash
Various herbs/spices
Plenty of live food recipe books
Beautiful dishes for serving guest and eating fancysometimes

26

Your Garden

Whether you have boxes in your window a seal, a small section set aside in your back yard or on the side of the house or an acre or two of plots, gardening is an excellent addition to your desire to prepare live foods.

The beginning process for starting a garden will be to actually select the size that you desire and what type of garden would you like to have, an herb garden, a vegetable garden, an orchard or a combination of all.

I share with you the type of gardening that I know best which is with the raised beds in the backyard. I have grown everything from okra, tomatoes, squash, green beans, eggplant, bell peppers, carrots, watermelons, cantaloupes, parsley, basil, mustard greens, collard greens, kale, bananas, peaches, lemons, cabbage, cucumbers, mint, strawberries, sunflowers, apples and avocados.

Each year, with the largest planting season being in early spring and continuing through the summer, we start the raised beds by laying down black and white newspaper to eliminate grass growth. Then, frames are made for the beds with 2 x 4 boards. Each year, we replenish the soil with composted soil or naturally nourished soil from the soil lot. Beds should contain about 6-8 inches of good soil. Seeds or sprouts are then implanted and the watering and growing begins. If you live in a hot weather climate, the garden will need to be watered every day with the exception of good rainy days.

Learn the importance of having the ability to grow and sustain a garden for optimum health and survival. YOU SHOULD BE ABLE TO FEED YOURSELF AND YOUR FAMILY.

Plant an herb garden of what is common to you where you are; basil, dandelion, parsley, green onion, sunflowers, rosemary, etc.

Herb gardens are one of the easiest types of gardens that one can grow. Most herbs will grow naturally without much cultivation. Herbs like to grow without much structure. For example; basil grows in abundance in the summer time. Just throw the seeds in a little turned soil, pat, water and it grows beautifully.

Teaching the Children About Food

If your child attends public school or even if you home school and allow them to indulge in only certain parts of the secular world (TV, internet, video games, etc.), teaching them about food is going to be beneficial for them throughout their lives. Our children are growing up in a world that bombards them with destructive dietary habits consistently. It is our duty as parents to equip them with love, proper nourishment, a sound mind, a healthy body, a vessel filled with self-esteem and the confidence to perform their best in a system that is not designed with them in mind.

It is ideal to prepare your child healthy meals each day. A proper nutritious meal will include a grain, two vegetables, a bean, legume, nut or seed. They should also be given seasonal fruit daily. However, if they must eat outside of the home, instruct them on what to eat and what not to eat. They will listen because you have taught them and you lead by example the importance of taking care of the body by eating the correct foods. Educate yourself on what the body needs certain foods for.

Take your children grocery shopping with you or down to your local organic farm and show them how to select the best foods for their bodies. Include them in meal preparation time and allow them to also prepare the meals for the family according to their creativity. I guarantee some interesting meals will come about. Learn and teach your child the importance of the balance between eating live foods and cooked foods. With a family's eating habits consisting of a majority of live foods, you will cut out a lot of illnesses and dis-ease in the family's lifestyle. Whole children are happy and healthy.

Recipes for Holistic Health

Brain Power Starters

It is important to give your brain a boost of energy in the morning to start your day. Upon waking, the body has just come out of a regeneration process.

During the hours of 5:00 AM and 7:00 AM, the colon is the dominant organ in the body and if the body is in order with its natural cycle you will eliminate waste during these hours. From 7:00 AM to 9:00 AM, the earth cycle of the body begins and the dominate organ is the stomach. Therefore, morning nourishment is vital for the brain and body function throughout the day.

Your brain needs proteins and good fats to jump start itself in the morning. Therefore, oats, grains, nuts, nut juices and protein rich greens are excellent for starting the day.

Adding a little bit of fruit for flavor and your natural sugars is also a good way to raise the energy level in the morning.

Starting your morning with juicing is excellent to get some much needed nutrients assimilated for your daily activities.

Coconut Water

One young coconut with the green hull shaved off. Pierce a hole in the top large enough for a straw to fit through. Insert straw and enjoy.

Nutrients: beta carotene, B complex vitamins, protein, iodine and good fat.

Body Nourishment : Coconut water is full of electrolytes for maximum hydration of the body. Nourishes the digestive system, body tissues, it can rid the body of tapeworms, boost male sexual fluids, treat kidney stones and intestinal worms.

Apple Juice

Juice 2 apples of your choice (Gala, Red, McIntosh, Green, Granny Smith, Jazz, etc.) to produce about 4 – 8oz of juice. Add the same amount of filtered or spring water and drink immediately for maximum nutritional use.

Nutrients: beta-carotene, calcium, phosphorus, potassium, silicon, vitamin B and C.

Body Nourishment: Apples are anti-bacterial, anti-inflammatory, antiviral, acts as an astringent, diuretic, stabilizes blood sugar and assists in good digestion and weight loss. Other areas of nourishment include colon health by reducing inflammation, diarrhea and constipation. Eating apples help to clean your teeth and promote healthy gums. For the internal organs, apple benefits the arteries, liver, gallbladder, lungs, lymphatic system and help ease the symptoms and heal gout, asthma, morning sickness and removes radiation and toxins from the body.

Beets Juice

Juice 4 small or 2 large sized beets to produce 4 – 8oz. of juice and add an equal amount of filtered or spring water and drink immediately for maximum nutritional use.

Nutrients: calcium, beta-carotene, fiber, folic acid, iron, manganese, phosphorus, potassium, sodium, vitamin A, B complex and C.

Body Nourishment: Helps increase oxygen intake, and promotes healthy blood through building and cleansing, contains anticancer properties. Beets enhance the kidneys, colon, bladder, liver detoxification and spleen. Beets have been used to reverse anemia, constipation, hepatitis, acne and low blood sugar.

Broccoli Juice

Juice 4 cups of broccoli to produce 2 – 6 oz. of juice and add 1 cup of filtered or spring water and drink immediately for maximum nutritional use.

Nutrients:beta-carotene, fiber, folic acid, boron, calcium, chromium, iron, magnesium, phosphorus, potassium, protein, selenium, sulphur, vitamins A, B2, B6, C, E and K.

Body Nourishment: Excellent anticancer properties and has stimulating effects on the immune system. Broccoli also helps prevent constipation, lowers high blood pressure, eyesight, stimulates weight loss and protects against toxemia.

Cabbage Juice

Juice 4 cups of cabbage for 2 – 4 oz. of juice and add an equal amount of filtered or spring water and drink immediately for maximum nutritional use.

Nutrients:beta-carotene, biotin, calcium, folic acid, fluorine, histamine, iodine, iron, manganese, magnesium potassium, protein, sulphur, Vitamins B1, B6, C, K and U.

Body Nourishment: Reduces risk of cancer, improves the body's ability to detoxify, effective in the treatment of ulcers and is good for the digestive system.

Carrots Juice

Juice 5 carrots for 2 – 4 oz. of juice, drink and enjoy.

Nutrients:beta-carotene, biotin, calcium, fiber, pectin, phosphorus, potassium, thiamine, vitamins A, B6, C and K.

Body Nourishment: Nourishes the cardiovascular system, carrots work as an antioxidant, they are good for the bladder, cervix, larynx, lungs, prostate, colon and esophagus by protecting these organs against cancer.

Celery Juice

Juice 3 stalks of celery for 2 – 4 oz. of juice; add an equal amount of spring or filtered water and drink immediately for maximum nutritional use.

Nutrients:beta carotene, calcium, chlorophyll, fibre, folic acid, magnesium, potassium, silica, sodium and vitamins B1, B2, B6 and C.

Body Nourishment: Benefits treatment of arthritis and gout, helps to activate white blood cells, supports the toning of the vascular system, provides electrolytes to the body, lowers blood pressure and cholesterol, and is useful in preventing migraines.

Cucumber Juice

Juice 2 cucumbers for 2 – 4 oz. of juice and drink immediately for maximum nutritional use.

Nutrients :beta carotene, calcium, chlorophyll, fiber, folic acid, magnesium, phosphorus, potassium, silica and vitamins A, C and E.

Body Nourishment: Cucumber strengthens the connective tissue in muscles, tendons, ligaments, cartilage and bone. It reduces swelling under the eyes and helps with sunburn. Cucumber is good for the skin.

Kale Juice

Juice 5 leaves of kale for 2 – 4 oz. of juice add an equal amount of spring or filtered water and drink immediately for maximum nutritional use.

Nutrients: beta carotene calcium, chlorophyll, copper, folic acid, iron, manganese potassium, sulfur and vitamins B6, C and E.

Body Nourishment: Kale has anti-cancer properties and is very high in chlorophyll which is excellent for healthy hemoglobin.

Mango Juice

Peel and slice 2 ripe mangos off the seed and place into a blender, add 1 -2 cups of water depending on the desired thickness and blend well. Drink and enjoy.

Nutrients: amino acids, beta carotene, calcium, iron, magnesium, niacin, pectin, potassium, vitamins C and E.

Body Nourishment: Mango works as an antiseptic, diuretic, and as a laxative. Mango is also used to treat anemia, cysts, fever, hypertension, indigestion, kidney inflammation, respiratory ailments and a weak digestive system.

Papaya Juice

Juice ½ papaya for 2 – 4 oz. of juice, add an equal amount of filtered or spring water and drink immediately for maximum nutritional use.

Nutrients: beta carotene, calcium, magnesium, potassium, protease, vitamins C and E.

Body Nourishment: Papaya is good for the digestive system, the lungs, menstrual irregularities and colon health. Papaya can also help reduce the risk of stroke and heart attack. It also enhances hair growth, healthy nails and skin.

Pineapple Juice

Juice ½ pineapple for 2 - 4oz. of juice, add an equal amount of filtered or spring water and drink immediately for maximum nutritional use.

Nutrients: beta carotene, carbohydrates, fiber, magnesium, manganese, potassium, vitamins B complex and C.

Body Nourishment: Pineapples are rich in digestive enzymes, is anti-inflammatory, anti-bacteria, anti-viral, diuretic, blood enhancer, strengthens bones, protects against and reduces edema, constipation, expels intestinal worms and prevents sore throat.

Kale Strawberry Juice

2 cups of filtered or spring water
10 strawberries fresh
5 leaves of kale

Juice kale and strawberries through the juicer and combine with water stir and serve.
Serves 1

Nutrients: beta carotene, calcium, iron, copper, manganese, folic acid, iodine, vitamins B1, B2, B6, C, E and K.

Body Nourishment: Nourishes the respiratory system, protects against arthritis, asthma, cancer, heart disease and inflammation.

Carrot Beet Delight

8 -12 organic carrots
1 small to medium beet cleaned and peeled
1 organic cucumber
2 cups of spring water

Juice vegetables through the juicer, combine with water and serve.
Serves 4

Nutrients: beta carotene, calcium, iron, copper, manganese, fiber, folic acid, magnesium, chlorophyll, silica, potassium, vitamins A, B complex,C, E and K.phosphorus, sodium,

Body Nourishment: Helps increase oxygen intake, builds the blood, regulates the body's pH, high in antioxidants, nourishes the eyesight, respiratory system and protects against macular degeneration. Beets enhance the kidneys, colon, bladder, liver detoxification and spleen. Beets have been used to reverse anemia, constipation, hepatitis, acne and low blood sugar.

Cool Green Drink

5 leaves of kale
1 cup of spinach
1 cucumber
2 cups of spring water

Juice vegetables through the juicer, combine with water and serve.
Serves 2

Nutrients:beta carotene, calcium, iron, copper, manganese, folic acid, magnesium, chlorophyll, silica, potassium, vitamins A, B1, B2, B6, C, E and K.

Body Nourishment: Regulates the body's pH, high in antioxidants, nourishes the eyesight, respiratory system and the connective tissue, builds muscles, ligaments, tendons, cartilage and bone, protects against macular degeneration, cataracts, cancer, skin, swelling and burns.

Goddess Healing Potion

1 oz. of wild blue green algae juice
2 oz. ginger juice fresh squeezed
5 oz. natural water
1 tsp. agave nectar

Stir in a 12oz. glass and enjoy the rich tantalizing burst of energy!
Serves 1

Nutrients:B-12, B complex, chlorophyll, protein, iron, beta-carotene, calcium, Vitamin C and A, folic acid, biotin, niacin

Body Nourishment: Alleviates congestion, aids in digestion, use for vitamin and mineral deficiencies, heavy metal poisoning, purifies the blood, stops inflammation, rejuvenates cells, anemia, obesity, dermatitis, yeast over growth, depression, enhances memory, supports the hypothalamus, the pineal and pituitary glands, contains phycocyanin which are pigments that prevent cancer clusters and inhibits the AIDS virus.

Almond Milk

1 cup raw almonds (soaked)
4 cups spring water
1 tsp. cinnamon
1 dash vanilla extract

**In a blender, combine all ingredients and blend
well. You may choose to strain or not.
Serves 4**

Nutrients: protein, calcium, iron, magnesium, zinc,
potassium and vitamin E.

Body Nourishment: Excellent brain and bone food
to get you started for the day. Almonds are good for
the lungs, liver, nervous system, improves energy
and sexual vitality.

Power Boost Almond

1 cup of almonds (soaked overnight)
1 organic banana (frozen for thicker smoothie)
¼ cup of organic oats
3 cups organic almond milk
1 tbsp. flaxseed oil
1 tbsp. organic agave nectar or agave to taste

Combine all ingredients and blend well. Pour and enjoy. This is an excellent source of morning protein.
Serves 2 - 4

Nutrients:folic acid, glucose, fructose, calcium, iron, zinc, magnesium, potassium, protein, omega-3, omega-6 fatty acids, vitamins A, B, B6, C and E.

Body Nourishment: This smoothie is excellent food for your brain, digestive system, muscles and bones. It improves stamina and works to increase your energy level. It nourishes the lungs, nervous system and liver. It increases sexual vitality and contains a large amount of protein.

Creamy Almond Peach Bliss

2 cup of almond milk
2 organic bananas (frozen for thicker smoothie)
¼ cup of almond butter
1 cup peaches (fresh or frozen)
agave to taste

Combine all ingredients and blend well. Pour and enjoy. This is an excellent source of morning protein.
Serves 2 - 4

Nutrients:fiber,folic acid, glucose, fructose, calcium, iron, zinc, magnesium, potassium, protein, vitamins A, B, B6, C and E.

Body Nourishment: This smoothie is excellent food for your brain, digestive system, muscles and bones. It improves stamina and works to increase your energy level. It nourishes the lungs, nervous system and liver. It increases sexual vitality and contains a large amount of protein.

Mango Munch

1 large organic mango (sliced off seed)
1 cup of pineapple (cubed)
¼ cup of organic oats
2 cups rice milk
1 tbsp. flaxseed oil
1 tbsp. organic agave nectar

Combine all ingredients and blend well. Pour and enjoy.
Serves 2 - 4

Nutrients: Beta-carotene, calcium, iron, potassium, magnesium, manganese, fiber, niacin, pectin, lysine, protein, omega-3, omega-6 fatty acids, vitamins B, B6, B-complex, C and E.

Body Nourishment: Nourishes the digestive system with its laxative and diuretic properties. It is good for nausea, sea sickness, indigestion and fever. Pineapple has multidimensional nutritious properties including expelling parasites and intestinal worms, anti-viral, anti-bacterial, circulatory system assistance, hypertension and excessive menstrual flow. Oats and pineapples are a beneficial food for multiple sclerosis.

Avocado Heaven

½ small avocado
1 organic banana
1 cup pineapple (cubed)
½ cup mango slices
2 cups rice milk

Add preferred sweetener if needed. Combine all ingredients and blend well. Pour and enjoy. Serves 2

Nutrients:beta-carotene, calcium, iron, potassium, magnesium, manganese, fiber, niacin, pectin, lysine,vitamins B, B6, B-complex, C and E.

Body Nourishment: Nourishes and aids the circulatory system and protects against blood clots, aids in relieving ailments of the respiratory system such as bronchitis and asthma. Excellent for sleep disorders including insomnia. Balances the liver and relieves hemorrhoids.

Blueberry Smoothie

1 banana
1½ cup fresh blueberries
2 tbsp. agave nectar sweetener
2 cups almond milk

Blend ingredients until smooth.
Serves 2

Nutrients:protein, iron,zinc,calcium, potassium, magnesium, biotin and fiber sodium, pectin, glucose, fructose, sucrose, vitamins B2, B6, C and E.

Body Nourishment: Improves vision, heart function, balances body fluids, improves blood pressure, reduces risk of stroke and lowers LDL, Nourishes the digestive system and urinary tract. Protects against Alzheimer's disease, protects the brain against oxidative stress, macular degeneration, protects against cataracts and glaucoma, varicose veins, hemorrhoids and peptic ulcers, relieves diarrhea, constipation and normalizes bowel function

Blackberry Smoothie

1 cup strawberries fresh or frozen
1 cup blackberries fresh or frozen
2 cups water or your favorite nut milk
1 banana
2 tbsp. of agave
1 tbsp. of a Green Mix of choice

Blend until smooth.
Serves 2

Nutrients:iodine, protein, glucose, fructose, sucrose, iron, zinc, potassium, chlorophyll, vitamins B1, C and K

Body Nourishment: Nourishes the digestive system, protects against high blood pressure,heart disease, inflammation, and cancer.

Strawberry Cashew Delight

½ cup strawberries fresh or frozen
2 cups of your favorite nut milk
2 bananas
2 tbsp. of cashew butter
2 tbsp. of agave or agave to taste.

Blend all ingredients until smooth and serve.
Serves 2

Nutrients:iodine, protein, glucose, fructose, sucrose, iron, zinc, potassium, chlorophyll, vitamins B1, C and K

Body Nourishment: Nourishes the digestive system, protects against high blood pressure, heart disease, inflammation, and cancer.

Kale Smoothie

2 cups pineapple fresh or frozen
1 banana
2 cups almond milk
2 leaves of kale

Blend until smooth to desired consistency.
Serves 2

Nutrients:beta carotene, calcium, iron, copper, phosphorus, potassium, sodium, manganese, protein, vitamins B1, B2, B6, C and E.

Body Nourishment: Nourishes the respiratory and digestive systems. Protects against sinusitis, carpal tunnel syndrome, heart disease, anti-inflammatory, anti-cancer, sore throat, arthritis, gout and speeds recovery from surgery.

Mean Green Smoothie

1 cup spinach
½ cup of organic oats
½ mango
½ cup of strawberries
1 banana
2 tbsp. agave nectar
2 tbsp. of a Green formula of your choice
3 cups of filtered or spring water

Combine all in the blender and mix well.
Serves 4

Nutrients:calcium, protein, copper, phosphorus, selenium, magnesium, iron, zinc, potassium, manganese, boron, dietary fiber, vitamins B1, B2, B6 and C.

Body Nourishment:Protects against heart disease, diabetes, lowers cholesterol, acts as a stool softener, anti-cancer and balances the body's pH.

Oats and Apple Granola Bars

1 gala apple organic (cored and chopped)
½ cup organic quick oats
¼ cup almond, soaked overnight/at least 2 hours
6 medium dates (pitted)
½ tsp. cinnamon
½ cup raisins
½ cup coconut, shredded (optional)

Lightly chop the almonds and dates in a food processor. Add the chopped apples and spices and pulse until it is a chunky granola texture. Stir in the remaining ingredients and shape into bars. Dehydrate for 5 hours or until firm.
Serves 6

Nutrients:calcium, iron, copper, phosphorus, selenium, magnesium, zinc, potassium, manganese, boron, dietary fiber, protein, vitamins B1, B2, B6 and C.

Body Nourishment:Protects against heart disease, diabetes, lowers cholesterol, stool softener, anti-cancer and balances the body's pH.

Strawberry Almond Swirl

2 bananas
½ cup almonds (soaked)
1 cup strawberries
4 tbsp. agave nectar
2 tbsp. coconut oil

Combine almonds, bananas, half of the strawberries, 2 tbsp. of the agave nectar and the coconut oil in the food processor until you have a creamy pudding. *(add a little almond milk if too thick)*

In the blender, add the remaining strawberries and agave nectar and blend to a red sauce, after pudding is put in the bowls for serving, drop a spoon full of strawberry sauce in and swirl for presentation and an extra wow of flavor.
Serves 2

Nutrients: Protein, calcium, iron, magnesium, zinc, potassium, vitamin B6, C and E.

Body Nourishment: Improves energy, increase sex hormone production, aids the digestive system, assist in reversing alcoholism, purifies blood, acts as a liver tonic, protects against anemia, constipation, high blood pressure, jaundice and lowers fever.

Blueberry Bars

1 cup raw almonds (soaked)
½ cup shredded coconut
6 medjool dates
1 cup fresh blueberries
Agave to taste

In a food processor combine almonds and dates until processed well. In a bowl add agave, coconut shreds and blueberries. Stir ingredients together then shape your blueberry mix into bars and dehydrate for 3 - 5 hrs. Serves 4 - 6

Nutrients: beta-carotene, calcium, iron, copper, magnesium, iron, zinc, potassium, boron, dietary fiber, vitamins B1, B2, B6, C and E.

Body Nourishment: Protects against stomach ulcers, bronchitis and anemia. Helps regenerate the pancreas, lowers cholesterol and is a powerful antioxidant. Excellent brain and bone food and is good for the lungs, liver, nervous system and sexual vitality.

Sweet Oats Pancakes

2 bananas
½ cup oats blended to a meal
¼ tsp. cinnamon
4 medjool dates (soaked)

Peel and mash bananas in a bowl, pour in blended oats, blend dates as close to a liquid as possible and add to other ingredients in bowl and sprinkle in cinnamon. Mix well with a mixing spoon.

When mixed well, scoop with serving spoon a generous amount onto plate and shape as a pancake. Allow to stand for about 15 minutes to naturally crust over or place in dehydrator for 45 minutes to 1 hour if desired.
Serves 2 - 4

Nutrients: protein, calcium, fructose, potassium, pectin, folic acid, copper, magnesium, iron, boron, fiber, B-complex and vitamin C.

Body Nourishment: Works as a spleen, blood and energy tonic. Treats anemia, stimulates the colon, prevents sore throats, coughs and bronchitis. Increases energy, assists in reversing drug addictions, depression and paralysis.

Midday Magic for Maximum Health

The Best Veggie Sandwich In the World

2 slices sprouted bread
½ organic cucumber
1 organic tomato
2 whole leaves of organic green leaf or romaine lettuce
1 avocado, alfalfa sprouts
¼ tsp. garlic powder
¼ juice of a lemon

Slice cucumber long and thin. Slice tomato sandwich style. Dress your bread if desired. Lay on the lettuce, tomato, cucumber, alfalfa sprouts. Remove avocado from shell, mash and mix in a bowl with garlic powder, lemon juice and desired seasons. Top alfalfa sprouts with avocado mix, close sandwich, cut in half and enjoy. Increase ingredients based on number of people to serve.

Nutrients: beta-carotene, folic acid, calcium, iron, potassium, sulfur, silicon, chlorophyll, histamine, lycopene, fluorine, copper, lecithin, vitamins B, B6, B-complex C, E and K.

Body Nourishment: Nourishes the respiratory system, helps with indigestion, weight gain, relieves constipation, kills tapeworms, assists in reversing diabetes and high blood pressure, balances liver function and soothes the bladder, anti-bacterial and anti-viral properties, reverses erectile dysfunction, has anti-aging properties, boosts your enzymes with alfalfa sprouts.

Veggiladas

8 organic green leaf lettuce leaves for wrapping
2 ears of corn
¼ cup of chopped cilantro
1 tomato (diced)
1 large avocado (diced)
1 tsp. chili powder
½ cup chopped red peppers
1 tsp. Vegit Seasoning

Set lettuce aside for wrapping.

In a large bowl, mix all ingredients well making sure some of the avocado cubes get smashed.

Put a small amount of mixture into each lettuce leaf. Add your favorite salsa or pico de gallo to each veggilada to taste and wrap.
Serves 8

Nutrients:beta-carotene, folic acid, calcium, iron, potassium, silicon, chlorophyll, fluorine, copper, lecithin, phosphorus, protein, omega-3, omega-6 fatty acids, zinc, vitamins B1, B6, B-complex C, E and K.

Body Nourishment: Nourishes the digestive system, cardiovascular system, nervous system and reproductive system. Helps with insomnia, stress and sexual addictions. Builds blood, bones and muscles. Prevents constipation, lubricates lungs and protects against ulcers.

Vegan Pizza

1 zucchini
½ yellow bell pepper
¼ red onion
½ bunch of broccoli
A handful of Black olives (sliced)
1 cup cherry tomatoes

Dice all vegetables and set aside

Cashew Cheese
2 cups raw cashews (soaked)
½ cup spring water
1 tsp. sea salt
2 tbsp. lemon juice
1 tsp. mustard powder
3 tbsp. nutritional yeast

Combine all ingredients in the food processor and process for 2 - 3 minutes until thick and creamy.

Marinara Sauce
2 or 3 medium tomatoes, cut in quads
1 cup sun dried tomatoes (soaked or in olive oil)
3 cloves garlic
1 tbsp. lemon juice
½ - 1 tsp. sea salt
2 tbsp. Italian seasoning mix
¼ cup fresh basil
3 tbsp. agave nectar
3 tbsp. extra virgin olive oil

Combine all ingredients in a blender until smooth.

Spread marinara evenly and thick over organic whole wheat pizza crust, sprouted pita bread or dehydrated flax crust. Then drop on veggies evenly around the pizza and top with cashew cheese. Slice as desired.
Serves 6

Nutrients:sulfur, beta-carotene, folic acid, calcium, protein, copper, phosphorus, magnesium, iron, zinc, potassium, dietary fiber, vitamins B1, B2, B6, C and E.

Body Nourishment:Protects against heart disease, stroke, kidney stress, bladder disorders, obesity, ulcers and cataracts. Good for muscle building and as an anti-inflammatory and diuretic.

60

Basil Spring Rolls

1 cup cabbage
½ cup purple cabbage
2 avocados
2 tbsp. Namashoyu
1 tbsp. garlic powder
1 tbsp. fresh basil
½ fresh squeezed lemon juice
6 collard green leaves

Cut collard leafs off stems to produce two wraps per leaf.

Mix all other ingredients in a mixing bowl. Spread mix on collard leaves and roll.
Serves 6

Nutrients:beta-carotene, protein, folic acid, calcium, iron, potassium, sulfur, chlorophyll, fluorine, iodine, copper, lecithin, omega-3, omega-6 fatty acids, vitamins B1, B6, B-complex C, E, K and U.

Body Nourishment:Works as an antibiotic and has anti-viral properties. Nourishes the lungs, liver and stomach. Prevents obesity, skin disorders, and dental problems. Cabbage is excellent for eye infections, radiation exposure, tuberculosis, yeast infections and gout. Avocado nourishes the blood, balances liver function, and is super for the digestive system.

Vegan Kebobs

1 red bell pepper
1 yellow squash
2 cloves of garlic
½ red onion
¼ cup sesame oil
¼ cup of tamari

12 Kebob sticks

Slice veggies into bite size and cubed pieces. Mix sesame oil and tamari in a bowl and toss in veggies and stir to coat all veggies with the marinade. When veggies are well coated, begin to insert stick in whatever patterns you desire and arrange on a platter and serve.
Serves 6

Nutrients:beta-carotene, calcium, iron, potassium, sulfur, vitamins A, B6 and C.

Body Nourishment: Nourishes the liver, lungs, prevents cancer, lowers blood cholesterol, reduces high blood pressure, has anti-bacterial and anti-viral properties and alleviates nasal congestion.

Carrot Tuna Sandwich

12 organic carrots
¼ cup red bell peppers (diced)
¼ cup celery (diced)
2 nori sheets cut into flakes
3 tbsp. Vegginaise
2 tbsp. Braggs
Green leaf lettuce
Steak tomatoes
Alfalfa sprouts

Juice carrots and put carrot pulp in a mixing bowl. Put in all other ingredients and mix well, spread on sprouted bread with veggies and serve. Serves 4 - 6

Nutrients:beta-carotene, folic acid, calcium, potassium, magnesium, silica, sodium, fiber, chlorophyll, protein and vitamins C.

Body Nourishment: Nourishes the blood, detoxifies the liver. Protects against cancer, acne, diabetes, hypertension and insomnia.

Pecan NoriNut Rolls

2 cups raw pecan (soaked)
1 tbsp. pressed garlic
1 tbsp. oregano
1 tbsp. cumin (powdered)
1 tbsp. of grape seed oil
1 tsp. sea salt
1 tsp. cayenne pepper
2 cups shredded romaine lettuce
1 sliced avocados
1 cup alfalfa sprouts
6 sheets Nori Seaweed

In a food processor, add pecans and seasonings and mix until smooth. Spread the pate in the Nori sheet, add lettuce, sprouts and avocado. Wrap the seaweed sheet tightly and seal with water. Cut into bite sized coins and serve. Serves 6-12

Nutrients:beta-carotene, folic acid, calcium, iron, potassium, sulfur, chlorophyll, protein, omega-3, omega-6 fatty acids, vitamins A, B, C, E and K.

Body Nourishment: Nourishes the liver, lungs, prevents constipation, skin disorders and ulcers.

Zahra's Sunny Raw Nori Rolls

2 cups hulled sunflower seeds (soaked)
4 green onions (green parts)
¼ cup fresh parsley
½ lemon juice
¼ cup of water
2 tbsp. Bragg Liquid Aminos
4 cloves garlic (4 tsp.)
8 sheets of nori
1 carrot (peeled and sliced into thin strips)
1 cucumber (peeled and sliced into thin strips)
1 avocado thinly (sliced)
1 cup sprouts of your choice

In a food processor add sunflower seeds, green onions, parsley, lemon juice, liquid aminos, garlic, water and mix until creamy. Set aside.

On cutting board, lay out 1 nori sheet, spread 2 tbsp. sunflower pate on nori sheet. Stack carrot strip, cucumber strip, avocado slice and sprouts in narrow line 1 inch from long edge of nori sheet. Fold nori sheet over vegetables and roll sheet away from you as tightly as possible. Dab edge of nori sheet with water to seal and close. Repeat with remaining ingredients. Cut each roll into 6 bite-size pieces with serrated knife.
Serves 6

Nutrients:protein, beta-carotene, zinc, copper, lecithin, folic acid, calcium, iron, chlorophyll, phosphorus, potassium, selenium, sulfur, omega-3, omega-6 fatty acids, B complex, vitamin C and E.

Body Nourishment: Works as an antioxidant in the body and has antibiotic properties. Nourishes the digestive system in bowel function and cleanses the lymph system. Parsley is a good remedy for arthritis, gout, edema and kidney inflammation. Nourishes the respiratory system and dissipates headaches.

OMG Walnut Pate

1 lb. of walnuts soaked overnight
2 stalks of celery (diced)
1 large carrots
¼ yellow onion
2 cloves of garlic
¼ cup of flaxseed oil
¼ cup of brown miso
½ cup of fresh parsley
1 tbsp. of sage
1 tsp. of thyme and rosemary ground
1 tsp. of poultry seasoning (Sea Salt if needed)
1 avocado

In a food processor, chop walnuts, brown miso and flaxseed oil to a paste consistency. Place in a separate bowl. In a food processor, lightly chop celery, carrots, onion and add to bowl. Add chopped garlic, ground sage, thyme, rosemary, chopped parsley and poultry seasoning. Mash in avocado and mix everything together by hand. Mold nicely unto a platter and garnish.
Serves 8

Nutrients:protein, beta carotene, calcium, iron, phosphorus, potassium, protein sodium, pectin, selenium, sulfur, histamine, omega-3, omega-6 fatty acids, B complex vitamins, C and E.

Body Nourishment: Nourishes the immune, respiratory and digestive system. Protects against inflammation, balances liver function and soothes the bladder.

Veggie Fettu

3 Zucchini, peeled

With a vegetable peeler create long fettuccini style strands into the bowl. Rotate the zucchini and repeat slicing, stop at the seeds.

Marinara Sauce
2 tomatoes cut in quads
2 tbsp. agave nectar
¼ tsp. sea salt
½ tbsp. Italian herb seasoning
½ cup basil (fresh)
1 cup sun-dried tomato in olive oil or soaked
½ jalapeno pepper
2 medium garlic cloves

Blend ingredients until smooth but thick. Top zucchini with marinara sauce.
Serves 4

Nutrients:beta-carotene, folic acid, dietary fiber, manganese, selenium, phosphorus, niacin calcium, iron, potassium, sulfur, germanium, copper, protein, vitamins B6, C and K.

Body Nourishment: Good for hydration, respiration, headaches, kidney ailments and poor circulation. Acts as an antibacterial, de-wormer. Has anti-cancer properties by protecting against radiation and free radicals. Relieves constipation, high blood pressure, anti-bacterial and anti-viral.

Waluna

4 cups walnuts soaked over night
½ cup water
½ small white onion diced
2 stalks of celery
2 Tbsp. organic Kelp granules
½ cup sweet relish *(or relish to taste)*
3 Tbsp. of Veggienaise-grapeseed oil *(optional)*
Add a little Spring Water for pate consistency
1 Tsp. sea salt

Grind walnuts and celery in the food processor adding a little spring water at a time to achieve pate consistency. When pate consistency is reached, transfer to mixing bowl and add all other ingredients and mix well. Add more salt or relish to suit your waluna taste! *I like it with water crackers topped with romaine lettuce.*

Nutrients: protein,iodine,beta-carotene, calcium, chlorophyll, iron, phosphorus, potassium, sulfur, fiber, pectin, B complex vitamins, B6 and C.

Body Nourishment: Nourishes the brain, large intestines, the blood and whole body system.

Garden Kale Salad

1 bunch of organic kale greens
¼ cup red pepper (chopped)
1 tbsp. pressed garlic
1 carrot (shredded)
2 tbsp. extra virgin olive oil
1 tbsp. liquid aminos
½ lemon (juiced)
2 avocados (pitted and cubed)

Wash kale greens and tear the leaf from the stalk into very small pieces by hand. Place greens in a large mixing bowl along with the olive oil, lemon juice, garlic, seasoning and mix well. Add all other vegetables and mix. Serves 6

Nutrients:beta-carotene, calcium, chlorophyll,iron, phosphorus, potassium, sulfur, fiber, pectin, omega-3, omega-6 fatty acids, B complex vitamins, B6 and C.

Body Nourishment: Nourishes the respiratory, digestive, circulatory and immune systems. Protects against heart disease, Avocado is known as one of the super foods because it has a wonderful supply of most nutrients including good fats.

Garlic Kale Salad

1 bunch of organic kale greens
¼ cup tahini
1 tbsp. pressed garlic
1 tbsp. sesame seeds
1 tbsp. liquid aminos or to taste
½ lemon (juiced)

Wash kale greens and tear the leaf from the stalk into very small pieces by hand. Place greens in a large mixing bowl along with the tahini, lemon juice, garlic, seasoning and mix well.

Serves 6

Nutrients:beta-carotene, calcium, chlorophyll,iron, phosphorus, potassium, protein, sulfur, fiber, B complex vitamins, B6 and C.

Body Nourishment:Nourishes the respiratory, digestive, circulatory and immune systems. Protects against heart disease.

Cheezy Kale Salad

1 bunch of organic kale greens
½ cup Sundried tomatoes (diced)
1 tsp. garlic powder
1 tbsp. extra virgin olive oil (marinade massage)
1 tbsp. liquid aminos
2 tbsp. Nutritional Yeast (more to taste)

Wash kale greens and tear the leaf from the stalk into very small pieces by hand. Place greens in a large mixing bowl along with the olive oil, lemon juice, garlic, seasoning and mix well. Add all other vegetables and mix. Serves 6

Nutrients:beta-carotene, calcium, chlorophyll,iron, phosphorus, potassium, protein, sulfur, fiber, pectin, omega-3, omega-6 fatty acids, B complex vitamins, B6, B12 and C.

Body Nourishment: Nourishes the respiratory, digestive, circulatory and immune systems. Protects against heart disease,

Hot Greens

1 bunch of organic kale greens
8 sundried tomatoes in olive oil or soaked
½ habanera pepper
½ tbsp. flaxseed oil
½ tbsp. olive oil
1 tbsp. Braggs Liquid Amino Acids (or to taste)

Place all ingredients in a food processor, blend well and serve.
Serves 4

Nutrients:beta-carotene, folic acid, calcium, iron, potassium, sulfur, chlorophyll, protein, omega-3, omega-6 fatty acids, vitamins A, B, C, E and K.

Body Nourishment: Nourishes the liver, lungs, prevents constipation, skin disorders and ulcers. Kale assists with weight loss, joint problems and dental problems.

Warm Spinach Salad

1 lb. of organic baby spinach
1 organic avocado
1 organic tomato
2 tbsp. of organic virgin olive oil
1 tsp. of organic flaxseed oil
1 tbsp. of raw oats
1 tbsp. of Braggs Liquid Aminos

**Mix all ingredients in a large bowl. Mix with your loving hands well and serve.
Serves 6**

Nutrients:beta-carotene, folic acid, calcium, iron, potassium, sulfur, chlorophyll, fluorine, copper, lecithin, phosphorus, protein, oleic acids, amino acids, omega-3, omega-6 fatty acids, vitamins A, B6, B-complex C, E and K.

Body Nourishment: Nourishes the blood, prevents constipation, lubricates lungs, balances the liver, recommended for erectile dysfunction, insomnia and ulcers. Protects against stroke, heart disease and cataracts.

Yea Man Bulgur Wheat

2 cups of organic bulgur wheat
¼ organic parsley (from your herb garden ☺)
1 tbsp. of Spike seasoning
1 tbsp. of Braggs Liquid Aminos
1 tbsp. of dry Jamaican Jerk seasoning

Soak bulgur wheat until tender. Drain off excess water. Chop parsley finely. Mix all seasonings with parsley in salad bowl. Season to taste if needed.
Serves 6

Nutrients:beta-carotene, iron, magnesium, zinc, chlorophyll, vitamins B, B6, B-complex C and E.

Body Nourishment:Parsley is a beneficial remedy for arthritis, gout kidney inflammation, kidney stones and halitosis.

Couscous Dressing

1 cup of couscous
½ cup of shredded carrots
½ cup of finely diced red peppers
¼ cup of finely chopped parsley
1 tbsp. olive oil
1 tbsp. poultry seasoning
1 tbsp. ground sage
Braggs Liquid Aminos to taste

Cover the couscous with spring water, set aside and let it soak up all the water until light and fluffy; about 20 minutes. When all the water is absorbed, add all the remaining ingredients, mix well and serve.
Serves 4 - 6

Nutrients:beta-carotene, potassium, thiamine, chlorophyll, magnesium, calcium, zinc, folic acid, iron, dietary fiber, omega-9 fatty acid, vitamins A, B Complex, B6, C, E and K.

Body Nourishment:Works as an antioxidant and protects against cancer in the bladder, cervix, colon, larynx, esophagus and lungs. Good for the eyes, nerves, diabetes and prevents perspiration, asthma and arthritis.

Curry Cabbage

1 green cabbage (shredded)
1 red pepper (wedged)
½ yellow pepper (diced)
2 medium carrots (coined)
2 cloves garlic (pressed)
1 medium tomato (wedged)
1 tsp. liquid aminos
½ cup olive oil
1 tbsp. curry powder

In a large mixing bowl, combine all ingredients and toss well to marinade curry and oil over all ingredients.
Serves 4 - 6

Nutrients:beta-carotene, folic acid, calcium, iron, potassium, sulfur, chlorophyll, protein, vitamins A, B, C, E and K.

Body Nourishment: Nourishes the liver, lungs, prevents constipation, skin disorders and ulcers.

Plantain Salad

2 ripe plantains
1 stalk of green onion (chopped)
1 tbsp. Braggs
1 tbsp. curry powder
1 tsp. turmeric
½ cup soaked and sliced almonds

Peel and slice very ripe plantains. Cut into coins.
Chop green onions. Mix all ingredients, let chill
for 30 minutes and serve.
Serves 6

Nutrients:beta-carotene, folic acid, calcium, iron,
potassium, sulfur, chlorophyll, selenium, protein,
vitamins B, B6 and C.

Body Nourishment: Nourishes the Integumentary
system and the digestive system. Improves energy,
stamina, sleep and mood. Also used to relieve
constipation, depression, exhaustion, hypertension,
ulcers and hemorrhoids. The recipe has anti-viral
and anti-infection properties.

Akua's Favorite Asparagus

1 bunch of asparagus
½ juiced orange
½ orange thinly (sliced)
1 tbsp. agave nectar
1 tbsp. olive oil
1 tbsp. Bragg's Liquid Aminos

Lay asparagus on a platter. Pour on orange juice. Drizzle on oil. Drizzle on agave. Drizzle on liquid aminos. Top with orange slices and serve. Serves 6

Nutrients:beta-carotene, iodine, zinc, folic acid, calcium, iron, potassium, vitamins B, B1, C and E.

Body Nourishment: Nourishes the circulatory system. Cools fevers, inhibits tumor growth, works on kidney health and eliminates darkness under the eyes.

Okra and Tomato

½ lb. of fresh okra
2 tomatoes (diced)
2 fresh garlic cloves
¼ purple onion (sliced in thin strips)
2 tbsp. Braggs
1 tsp. basil flakes

Slice okra into small coins, dice garlic and dice tomatoes. Combine all ingredients in a bowl and mix well. Add Braggs or sea salt if desired. Serves 6

Nutrients:beta-carotene, calcium, iron, phosphorus, potassium, sodium, sulfur, lycopen, histamine, B complex, vitamins, C and E.

Body Nourishment: Nourishes the respiratory system. Protects against heart disease, cataracts and preserve the body's balance of fluids.

Green Beans on the Side

3 cups of green beans
2 tbsp. of Braggs
½ cup of sliced almonds
¼ cup of raisins

Soak green beans overnight. Combine all ingredients in a bowl and mix well.
Serves 6

Nutrients:beta-carotene, protein,calcium, iron, phosphorus, magnesium, potassium, sodium, pectin, zinc, antioxidants, B complex and vitamin C.

Body Nourishment: Nourishes the brain, bones, liver, respiratory system and nervous system.

Flax Seed Crackers

1 cup brown flax seeds
Spring water
Braggs to taste for seasoning

Pour flaxseeds into a wide bowl and pour enough spring water on them to slightly rise above the seed level and stir in seasoning. Allow mixture to sit about 20 minutes to absorb the water. It will turn slightly slimy similar to okra. Spread cracker mix on the bottom dehydrator tray or whichever tray you have that is not gridded. Dehydrate for 8 hrs or until crackers come out hard and crispy.
Serves 6

Nutrients:protein, omega-3 and omega-6 fatty acids, vitamins A, B and E.

Body Nourishment: Protects against heart disease, and nourishes the Integumentary, digestive and immune systems.

Salad Dressings

Salad dressings are truly a test of your creativity and by choice I never make the same one twice! There are few basics in salad dressings that will give you a unique tasty creation everytime.

1. A good blender.
2. Your preferred oil base.
3. Water for consistency.
4. Seasonings for flavor.
5. Veggie of choice for substance.
6. Avocado or cashews for creaminess.
7. And a lemon twist (optional).

Enjoy creating your own salad dressings and you never have to buy salad dressings again.

It Tastes Like Ranch Dressing

½ cup cashews (soaked)
½ cup spring water
1 tbsp. lemon juice
¼ tsp. garlic (pressed)
¼ tsp. onion powder
Sea salt to taste
1 tbsp. fresh basil
½ tbsp. fresh dill weed

Blend cashews, water, lemon, garlic and onion until smooth and creamy. Add basil and dill weed and pulse briefly just to chop and mix.
Serves 4

Zahra's Spinach Tahini Dressing

½ cup tahini
1 handful of spinach
3 tbsp. of tamari
2 cups of water
1 cup of raisins

Blend all ingredients till smooth and creamy
Serves 4

Ginger Garlic Dressing

2 cloves garlic (chopped)
1 tbsp. fresh ginger (chopped)
2 tbsp. NamaShoyu or Braggs
2 tsp. sesame oil
3 tsp. tahini
2 tbsp. olive oil

Blend, chill and serve.
Serves 4

Evening Curbs

Goddess Supreme Nourishment

4 leaves of romaine lettuce
1 handful of alfalfa sprouts
10 cherry tomatoes cut is halves
¼ cup red bell pepper sliced thin and long
½ cup of okra sliced in coins

Cover the whole plate with the alfalfa sprouts by pulling them loose. Thinly slice the romaine lettuce and as the next layer on the plate. Slice the okra as the next layer and top with the red bells and tomatoes. Set aside while you prepare the goddess dressing.

Goddess Dressing

2 tbsp. Olive oil
1 tbsp. Bragg liquid amino
1 tbsp. agave nectar
2 shakes of cayenne pepper
Add other herbs and spices to suit your tastes.

Mix all ingredients well in a cup. Pour over salad and enjoy.

Nutrients:beta-carotene, calcium, chlorophyll, iron, phosphorus, potassium, protein, sulfur, fiber, pectin, omega-3, omega-6 fatty acids, B complex vitamins, B6 and C.

Body Nourishment: Nourishes the respiratory, digestive, circulatory and immune systems.Protects against heart, disease bowel disorders and womb ailments.Olive oilis good fat.

A Bunch of Greens

1 bunch of collards
1 bunch of kale
2 tbsp. flaxseed oil
1½ tbsp. agave
2 fresh garlic cloves (pressed)
1 tsp. ground cumin

Cut washed greens from around the ribs down the center. Stack leaves and roll tightly, cut into thin coins and place in bowl. Combine remaining ingredients in a separate bowl and mix well into a dressing. When ready to serve, mix with greens and serve.
Serves 6

Nutrients:beta-carotene, calcium, chlorophyll,iron, phosphorus, potassium, sulfur, fiber, pectin, omega-3, omega-6 fatty acids, B complex vitamins, B6 and C.

Body Nourishment: Nourishes the respiratory, digestive, circulatory and immune systems, Protects against heart disease. Flaxseed has a wonderful supply of good fats.

Vegetti with Marinara

Marinara Sauce

2 large tomatoes
1½ red bell pepper
1 cup sun dried tomatoes
2 tsp. extra virgin olive oil
1 tsp. agave
1 – 2 cloves of garlic
1 tbsp. fresh basil (chopped)
Salt to taste, water to the end is needed

All the ingredients in food processor or blender and add water as needed.

Pasta

3 small zucchini

Make noodles with vegetable spiral slicer. Place noodles on paper towels to absorb moisture. Toss noodles with sauce and serve immediately. Serves 6

Nutrients:beta-carotene, folic acid, dietary fiber, iron, manganese, selenium, phosphorus, calcium, potassium, sulfur, germanium, copper, protein, vitamins B6, C and K.

Body Nourishment: Good for hydration, respiration, headaches, kidney ailments and poor circulation. Acts as a de-wormer. Has anti-cancer properties by protecting against radiation and free radicals, relieves constipation, high blood pressure, anti-bacterial and anti-viral.

Mixed Greens Delight

½ Napa cabbage
½ green leaf lettuce
¼ green cabbage
1 cup parsley leaves

Chop and layer greens in a salad bowl.

Green Delight Dressing

2 garlic cloves
4 green onion stalks
½ jalapeno pepper
1 small bunch cilantro
1 lime (juiced)
½ cup of water
½ tsp. sea salt (or to taste)
2 tsp. olive oil
½ tsp. cumin powder

Top greens with dressing on each individual plate.
Serves 6

Nutrients:beta-carotene, folic acid, calcium, iron, sulfur, iodine, protein, selenium, magnesium, iron, potassium, vitamins B1, B6, C, K and U.

Body Nourishment: Protects against breast cancer, heart disease, strokes, cataracts and diabetes.

Kerubo's Plantain Slaw

2 cups finely shredded green cabbage
1 cup shredded carrots
1 cup finely chopped broccoli
1 ½ cup plantain chopped in small quads
1 tbsp. agave nectar
2 tbsp. Veggienaise with grapeseed oil

**Mix all ingredients well, chill and serve.
Serves 6**

Nutrients:beta-carotene, folic acid, calcium, iron, potassium, sulfur, chlorophyll, protein, vitamins A, B, C, E and K.

Body Nourishment: Nourishes the liver, lungs, prevents constipation, skin disorders and ulcers.

Summer Green Rolls

10 green leaf lettuce leaves
1 cup of green peas (organic frozen)
2 avocados (diced)
1 stalk of celery thin sliced coins
½ lemon (juiced)
¼ cup of sesame oil
2 tsp. Braggs Liquid aminos

Rinse whole lettuce leaves and set to the side for drying. Place peas in a strainer and allow the filtered tap to run over them until thawed. Slice celery stalk into very thin coins. Dice avocado and cover with lemon juice. In a mixing bowl, combine celery, peas, sesame oil and lightly stir to coat with oil. Drop in avocado and Braggs and again lightly stir as to not mash the avocado.

Dip a table spoon full into each lettuce leaf, wrap, place on presentation tray and serve. Serves 5

Nutrients:beta-carotene, folic acid calcium, chlorophyll, iodine, iron, phosphorus, protein, magnesium, zinc, potassium, manganese boron, dietary fiber Omega-3 and Omega-6 fatty acids, vitamins B1, B6, C, E and K.

Body Nourishment: Helps to reduce swollen joints and good for the digestive, glandular, and excretory systems. Protects against high cholesterol, ulcers and obesity.

Dr. Derrick's Avocado Tacos

2 large ripe avocados
1 stalk of broccoli
1 tbsp. of fresh cilantro
1 large ripe salad tomato
½ lemon
1 tbsp. garlic powder
1 tbsp. Braggs
1 tbsp. chili powder
12 whole leaves of green leaf lettuce

Set lettuce a side, this is your taco shell. Slice broccoli off of stalk into mixing bowl into very small pieces. Open, pit and scoop out avocado into mixing bowl over broccoli. Chop up cilantro very fine and add to bowl. Dice tomatoes and add to bowl with all the listed seasonings and mix just enough for seasoning to blend in, yet avocado chunks still remain visible. When mixture is to your taste, scoop small spoons full in a lettuce leaf, wrap it up and enjoy. You may also add a topping of your favorite raw or homemade salsa.
Serves 6

Nutrients: beta-carotene, fiber, folic acid, calcium, iron, potassium, sulfur, chlorophyll, chromium, selenium, fluorine, copper, lecithin, phosphorus, protein, omega-3, omega-6 fatty acids, vitamins B2, B-complex C, E and K.

Body Nourishment: Nourishes the blood, prevents constipation, lubricates lungs, balances the liver, recommended for erectile dysfunction, insomnia, and ulcers. Protects against stroke, heart disease and cataracts.

Wakame Wonder

1 cup of organic dehydrated wakame
1 cup of organic petite green peas
1 lemon (juiced)
1 tbsp. garlic red pepper paste
Braggs to taste

Soak wakame for 1 hour. When all water is absorbed and leaves fluffy, combine all ingredients, mix well and serve.
Serves 6

Nutrients: beta-carotene, fiber, folic acid, calcium, iron, potassium, sulfur, chlorophyll, chromium, selenium, fluorine, copper, lecithin, phosphorus, protein, omega-3, omega-6 fatty acids, vitamins B2, B-complex C, E and K.

Body Nourishment: Nourishes the blood, prevents constipation, lubricates lungs, balances the liver, insomnia, and ulcers. Excellent digestive system aid.

Divine Desserts and Drinks

Chocolate Pudding

2 medium/large avocados
1 cup of water
¼ cup of cacao powder or more
(depends on the size of the avocados)
¼ cup of agave nectar
1 tsp. of vanilla extract

Combine all ingredients in a food processor and puree until smooth, adding a little more water if needed. More water will give you a thinner pudding.
Serves 4

Nutrients:beta-carotene, fiber, folic acid, calcium, iron, potassium, sulfur, chlorophyll, chromium, selenium, fluorine, copper, lecithin, phosphorus, protein, omega-3, omega-6 fatty acids, vitamins B2, B-complex C, E and K.

Body Nourishment:Nourishes the blood, prevents constipation, lubricates lungs, balances the liver, recommended for erectile dysfunction, insomnia, and ulcers. Protects against stroke, heart disease and cataracts.

Chocolate Covered Strawberry Pie

1 lb. fresh strawberries

Prepare the chocolate pudding recipe on page 95. Wash and take of the tops of 1 pound of fresh strawberries. Slice strawberries into very thin slices and begin to layer a glass pie dish. Leave a few strawberries whole for decorations. Once sliced strawberries are in place, pour pudding into pie dish and chill for an hour before serving. Serves 6

Nutrients: beta carotene, calcium, iron, copper, manganese, folic acid, iodine, vitamins B1, B2, B6, C, E and K, potassium, sulfur, chlorophyll, chromium, selenium, fluorine, copper, lecithin, phosphorus, protein, omega-3, omega-6 fatty acids, B-complex.

Body Nourishment: Nourishes the respiratory system, circulatory system, protects against arthritis, asthma, cancer, heart disease, prevents constipation, inflammationbalances the liver, recommended for erectile dysfunction, insomnia, and ulcers..

Chocolate Ball Surprise

2 cups walnut soaked at least two hours
1/3 cup organic cacao powder
8 medjool dates
1 tsp. vanilla extract

Combine walnuts, dates, cacao and process on high until well combined. The food processor should roll mixture into a ball. Gather up remaining mixture from processor bowl and shape onto the ball. Slice like a cake and serve with cute little decorations.
Serves 10

Nutrients:protein, calcium, potassium, zinc, boron, copper, magnesium, fiber and vitamins E.

Body Nourishment:Nourishes the brain, large intestines and the blood. This dessert is good for the whole body system.

Fruit Salad for Akua

2 gala apples
2 bananas
2 oranges
½ pineapple
1 cup of grapes
1 juiced lemon

Slice all fruit except lemon in bite sized pieces. Mix well. Pour on lemon juice. Mix well. Chill and serve. Serves 6

Nutrients: Rich in antioxidants, beta carotene, calcium, fiber, folic acid, iron, magnesium, manganese, phosphorus, potassium, vitamins B complex, B1, B6 and C.

Body Nourishment: Nourishes the respiratory, digestive and immune systems. These ingredients act as a great Detox formula for the body.

Raw Coconut Balls

1 cup raw pecan
1 cup chopped dates
¾ cup dried coconut
2 tbsp. of raw agave

Grind the nuts and dates together, combine into a bowl. Add the ½ the coconut. Add just enough agave so that when you are forming the balls, they retain their shape. When balls are shaped, roll around in remaining coconut to coat and serve.

Nutrients:protein, beta-carotene, calcium, copper, fiber, magnesium, iron, potassium, B complex and B6.

Body Nourishment: Nourishes the liver, lungs, prevents constipation, skin disorders and ulcers.

Banana Mango Mix With Raspberry Syrup

5 ripe organic bananas (coined)
2 mangos (cubed)
½ cup raspberries
2 tbsp. of agave

In a mixing bowl, combine bananas and mango together. Chill in fridge for 30 minute to an hour. In a blender, combine raspberries and agave to a nice even consistency. Place chilled fruit mix in chilled glass dish and top with raspberry syrup and serve.
Serves 6

Nutrients: beta carotene, Vitamins B6, C, E, calcium, iron, magnesium, potassium

Body Nourishment: Nourishes the digestive, muscular, circulatory, excretory and respiratory systems. The recipe is an excellent tonic for the kidneys and the liver.

Banana Mango Pie

2 cup raw walnuts (soaked 4-6 hrs)
1 cup medjool dates
8 ripe bananas (sliced)
5 strawberries
2 mangoes
4 tbsp. of agave
½ cup of coconut oil

Chop walnuts and dates in the food processor for 3 minutes. Remove from processor bowl and shape into pie crust dish. Combine mango, agave and coconut oil in the blender and blend to a puree. Begin to layer the banana slices in the pie crust and pour the mango syrup over the sliced bananas and place in the refrigerator for 3 hrs to set. Garnish the top of the pie with strawberry fans.

Nutrients:beta-carotene, calcium, iron, potassium, magnesium, vitamins B6, C and E.

Body Nourishment: Nourishes the digestive, muscular, circulatory, excretory and respiratory systems. The recipe is an excellent tonic for the kidneys and the liver.

Dr. Maat preparing Banana Mango Pie in a Veggie Delights Live Foods Class.

Beautiful Banana Mango Pie!

Binta's Pineapple Protein Pops

1 cup flax meal
1 cup almond pulp
½ cup pineapple pulp
½ cup agave or to taste

Mix all ingredients in a mixing bowl into to cookie dough batter consistency. Shape small wafer size round thins on baking pan and dehydrate in oven at lowest temperature until crisp. Make your favorite dipping syrup to accent your wonderful healthy snacks.

Nutrients:beta carotene, carbohydrates, fiber, magnesium, manganese, potassium, vitamins B complex, C and E, protein, calcium, iron, and zinc.

Body Nourishment: Pineapples are rich in digestive enzymes, is anti-inflammatory, anti-bacteria, anti-viral, diuretic, blood enhancer, strengthens bones, protects against and reduces edema, constipation, expels intestinal worms and prevents sore throat. Almonds are good for the lungs, liver, nervous system, improves energy and sexual vitality.

Pineapple Cheesecake
With Coconut Mango Sauce

3 cups of cashews soaked
1 cup almonds soaked
30 dates soaked
1½ cup soft young coconut meat
1 lemon juiced
1 tbsp. agave nectar
1 mango neatly sliced from seed
Spring water
1 cup of fresh pineapple cubed

Mix almonds and 20 dates in the food processor until well mixed consistency should be thick. Place in glass pie dish and press evenly to cover entire dish including the sides. Mix cashews, remaining dates, ½ cup of coconut meat, lemon juice and ½ cup of fresh pineapples in food processor and mix well, adding water bit by bit to desired consistency. Pour batter unto crust and shape.

Decorate top of cheesecake with mango slices and garnish.

In a blender mix remaining coconut meat, ½ of sliced mango and agave nectar to a sauce. Put in nice serving dish and chill.

Serve in thin pie slices with sauce topping.

Ginger Lemonade

5 lemons
1 ginger root
¼ cup agave nectar or agave to taste
1 qt. water

Juice lemons and ginger root in a regular juicer. Add juice to water along with agave nectar sweetener to suit your taste and serve.

Nutrients:potassium, folic acid, fructose and sucrose, vitamins B6 and C.

Body Nourishment: Dissolves gallstones, protects against cancer, eases gastrointestinal stress, acts as an anti-inflammatory, prevents motion sickness, nausea and vomiting.

Mojito Mami's

5 limes
12 fresh mint leaves (rolled to release flavor)
¼ tsp. cinnamon powered
1 cup agave nectar
1 ½ qt. spring or filtered water

Juice limes with a citrus juicer. Roll mint leaves along cutting board.In a glass pitcher or punch bowl, add juice to water along with agave nectar and cinnamon to suit your taste and serve.

Nutrients:potassium, folic acid, fructose and sucrose, vitamins B6 and C.

Body Nourishment: Dissolves gallstones, protects against cancer, eases gastrointestinal stress, acts as an anti-inflammatory, prevents motion sickness, nausea and vomiting.

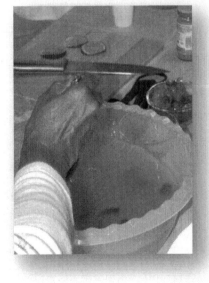

Transition Recipes

Veggie Deluxe Pizza

½ red bell pepper
½ yellow bell pepper
½ green bell pepper
½ red onion
½ yellow onion
2 stalks of green onion
3 cloves of garlic
1 cup broccoli
¼ cup of fresh parley

Heat oven to 200°. Prepare pizza crust of choice, a vegan variety, with marinara sauce from page 58 and set aside. Chop green onions and slice all other vegetables into very thin long slices. Sauteelightly with a little olive oil and top waiting pizza crust. Heat in oven for 10 – 15 minutes or until crust is warmed. Slice and serve. Serves 5

Southwestern Pizza

4 stalks of green onions
1 fresh corn on the cob
2 small avocados
2 hands full of cilantro
4 tomatoes
1 cup of pinto beans (cooked)
Garlic powder

Heat oven to 200°. Chop the veggies into pizza topping size, small but with a little chunk, green onions, cilantro and tomatoes. Set aside half of each to make your homemade salsa. Shave the corn from the cob and set aside with the other veggies. Prepare a homemade salsa by mixing half the veggies in a bowl and adding a little garlic powder to taste. Prepare your preferred pizza crust with marinara sauce from page 58.Sprinkle the tomatoes, corn and green onions on top. Place in the oven for 10 – 15 minutes. When pizza has heated remove and complete the toppings with avocado chunks, fresh cilantro and salsa.

Tofu Scramble

1 pack of extra firm tofu
1 red bell pepper
1 green bell pepper
½ yellow onion
1 tbsp. of turmeric (powdered)
1 tomato
Braggs to taste

Stir fry diced bell peppers and onion. Add tofu by hand crumbling into the skillet and add turmeric. When well mixed to an egg yellow color, remove from heat and add Braggs. Slice tomato and garnish in a circle around the edges of the tofu scramble.
Serves 4

Red Curry Stir Fry

1 pack of extra firm tofu (cubed)
2 cups of brown rice (cooked)
2 shredded carrots
½ onion (sliced)
2 cups of broccoli (chopped)
1 cup red bell peppers (diced)
Tamari to taste start with a few tbsp.
Organic red curry paste
Organic red pepper paste

In a non stick pan or with a small amount olive oil stir fry the cubed tofu to toughen the outside. Add veggies and stir fry together for two to three minutes. Once vegetables are cooked to your desired consistency, add rice and continue to stir. Add Tamari, red curry and pepper to taste.
Serves 6

Palm Oil Stew

1 medium eggplant
1 red bell pepper (large chunks)
2 small habanera peppers
1 yellow onion (slice in large chunks)
3 cups of fresh okra (sliced)
1 ½ cup of red palm oil
Braggs to taste
2 cups brown rice (cooked)

Chop vegetables and set to the side. In a large wok or pot, stir fry okra and eggplant until softened. Add palm oil and the rest of the vegetables. Allow mixture to cook for five minutes and add Braggs to taste. Serve over rice. Serves 5

Jama Jama

1 lb. of fresh spinach (baby or regular)
1 yellow onion (diced)
Braggs to taste

Stir fry onion in a frying pan. When onions are soft and browned, add spinach and Braggs. Stir over fire for 2 minutes and reduce heat. Continue warming to desired consistency. Remove from heat and serve.
Serves 4

Mediterranean Lentils

1 lb. lentils (soaked overnight)
1 yellow onion (diced)
2 carrots (coined)
2 stalks of celery (sliced)
2 tbsp. curry powder
2 tbsp. turmeric
2 tbsp. cumin
Braggs to taste

Prepare lentils by boiling 2 – 3 hours. When lentils are soft and edible, add vegetables and cook about 5 additional minutes. Remove from heat and add seasonings to taste. Serve warm as a soup or over couscous or rice.
Serves 6

Southern Split Pea Soup

1 lb. split pea
2 carrots (shredded)
1 yellow onion (diced)
½ tsp. cayenne
Braggs to taste

Boil split pea until done. Remove from heat and add shredded carrots, onions and seasoning. Cover for 30 minutes to allow the steam pressure to soften vegetables and cool.
Serves 6

Veggie Quinoa

2 cups of quinoa
1 carrot (grated)
½ cup red bell (diced)
½ cup green onion (diced)
2 tbsp. curry powder
2 tbsp. cumin

Bring to a boil, quinoa grains and spring water. Reduce heat to a simmer and cook for 10 minutes. Stir in vegetables and seasonings and continue to cook an additional 10 minutes or until quinoa is soft and edible. Add sea salt or liquid aminos to taste.
Serves 6

Plantain

2 ripe plantains
Choose plantains that have a lot of black on the skin and is soft to the touch.

2 cups of vegetable oil or red palm oil for pan frying

Heat vegetable oil in a frying pan. Peel and slice plantain in diagonals. Place slices in oil and fry to a light brown color and flip each slice of plantain over and continue the browning. Remove from pan to drain oil, cool and serve as an appetizer or side dish.
Serves 4

Meal Planner

Although most of the dishes presented here in Veggie Delights, should nutritionally be considered a meal, I have included this 5 Day Meal Planneras an example of combining some of the dishes for full course consumption. If this is your wonderful beginning with vegan/live foods it would be good to add one new dish a day as you work your way through the recipes.

Eating according to the natural rhythm of the body as it works in unison with the earth's consciousness, morning meals are light but hearty. Smoothies and plant based protein selections are the best.Your afternoon meal by holistic standards is your heaviest meal of the day. This will take planning going off to work daily. If food is consumed after 7pm it should be light and live.

Monday
❖ Morning Meal
  ❑ Power Boost Almond *(Smoothies are quick and easy for the morning rush)*

❖ Midday Magic
  ❑ The Best Veggie Sandwich In the World
  ❑ Okra Chips *(Sliced & seasoned to taste)*

❖ Evening Curb
  ❑ Warm Spinach Salad
  ❑ Plantain Salad

Tuesday
- ❖ Morning Meal
  - ❑ Mango Munch

- ❖ Midday Magic
  - ❑ Veggie Pizza
  - ❑ Mixed Greens Delight

- ❖ Evening Curb
  - ❑ Cous Cous Dressing
  - ❑ Garden Kale Salad
  - ❑ Vegan Kebobs

Wednesday
- ❖ Morning Meal
  - ❑ Avocado Heaven

- ❖ Midday Magic
  - ❑ Carrot Tuna Sandwich
  - ❑ Hot Greens

- ❖ Evening Curb
  - ❑ Vegetti with Marinara
  - ❑ A Bunch of Greens

Thursday
- ❖ Morning Meal
  - ❑ Blueberry Smoothie

- ❖ Midday Magic
  - ❑ Pecan Nori Nut Rolls
  - ❑ Cheezy Kale
  - ❑ Coconut Water

119

- ❖ Evening Curb
  - ❑ Kerubo's Plantain Slaw
  - ❑ Green Beans on the Side
  - ❑ Mojito Mami's

Friday
- ❖ Morning Meal
  - ❑ Strawberry Blessing

- ❖ Midday Magic
  - ❑ Waluna
  - ❑ Wakame Wonder
  - ❑ Flaxseed Crackers

- ❖ Evening Curb
  - ❑ Curry Cabbage
  - ❑ Okra and Tomato
  - ❑ Yea Mon Bulgur Wheat

Of course a live dessert can be added to any of the midday or evening meals.

Recommended Reading List

- *City of Wellness:The Journey Through Nutrition Kitchen with Nature's Pharmacy* by Queen Afua – Heal Thyself Publishing 2005

- *Rawsome* by Bridgitte Mars – Basic Health Publishing 2004.

- *The Joy of Living Live: a Raw Food Journey* by Zakhah – Communicators Press 2005.

- *Living in the Raw* by Rose Lee Calabro – Book Publishing Company 1998.

- *Raw: The Uncook Book* by Juliano – William Morrow 1999.

- *Vitamins and Minerals from A to Z* by Dr. Jewel Pookrum- A & B Publishing 1993.

About the Author

Dr. Akua, naturopath, spiritualist and master teacher, is the International Operations Director for A Life of Peace Wellness Institute, Inc., an international holistic health education and wellness non-profit organization. She is also the author of *Akwaaba! : Dr. Akua's Ghanaian Vegan Cuisine*, *Medical Astrology: From the Minds of the Ancients*, *Metaphysics of the Feminine Divine*, and *Dr. Akua's Way to Wellness: 28 Day Regeneration Programs*. Dr. Akua has shared the gifts of her works with the international communities of the USA, Canada, The Caribbean, Israel, The Philippines, England and Ghana.

An outstanding educator for 20+ years, Dr. Akua holds degrees and certifications in Naturopathy, Education, Telecommunications, Metaphysics, Hypnotherapy, Iridology, Reiki, Shiatsu, Colon Hydrotherapy and African Nutritional Science.

At A Life of Peace Wellness Institute Dr. Akua currently teaches classes in naturopathy, Sacred Goddess Temple Rites of Passage, Shiatsu, nutrition, holistic health business, live foods preparations, reiki, natural hair care, and many areas of alternative health options.

Dedicated to issues of Pan African Empowerment and Health,Dr. Akua has worked on family empowerment and healing as a spiritual counselor and Holistic Health Consultant and continues to enhance her spirit through the many avenues of consciousness elevation.

Dr. Akua currently resides in Ghana to establish Divine Life Sanctuary: The Pan African Village. The nurturer of three SUNS who are the mirror of the life she has lived, she shares these accomplishments with her divine reflection of 24 years Dr. Chenu.

Dr. Akua is available for Live Foods Classes and Retreats.

Made in the USA
Columbia, SC
16 November 2017